THE
WINE-LOVER'S
RECORD BOOK

THE
WINE-LOVER'S
RECORD BOOK

JANE HUGHES

PEONY PRESS

This edition is published by Peony Press, an imprint of Anness Publishing Ltd, Hermes House, 88–89 Blackfriars Road, London SE1 8HA; tel. 020 7401 2077; fax 020 7633 9499
www.peonypress.com; www.annesspublishing.com

If you like the images in this book and would like to investigate using them for publishing, promotions or advertising, please visit our website www.practicalpictures.com for more information.

Publisher: Joanna Lorenz
Project Editor: Joanne Rippin
Design: Prue Bucknall and Ruth Prentice

ETHICAL TRADING POLICY
Because of our ongoing ecological investment programme, you, as our customer, can have the pleasure and reassurance of knowing that a tree is being cultivated on your behalf to naturally replace the materials used to make the book you are holding. For further information about this scheme, go to www.annesspublishing.com/trees

All rights reserved. No part of this publication may be reproduced, stored in a retrieval system, or transmitted in any way or by any means, electronic, mechanical, photocopying, recording or otherwise, without the prior written permission of the copyright owner.

A CIP catalogue record for this book is available from the British Library

© Anness Publishing Ltd 1997, 2010

PUBLISHER'S NOTE
Although the advice and information in this book are believed to be accurate and true at the time of going to press, neither the authors nor the publisher can accept any legal responsibility or liability for any errors or omissions that may be made.

The publishers would like to thank the following libraries for providing pictures: Bridgeman Art Library: p 29 The Tasting: Servers bringing Wine by Jan Breughel. Cephas Picture Library: pp 2, 7, 8, 10, 13, 14, 16, 18, 19, 21bl, 23, 27, 28, 35, 37t, 37br, 39, 41, 47, 50b, 50tr, 62, 63. Fine Art Photographic Library: pp 7 His Favourite Bin by Walter Dendy Sadler, courtesy of N R Omell Gallery, London; 9 The Butler's Glass by Walter Dendy Sadler; 22 The Chef's Birthday by Andrea Landini; 31 Before the Orgy by Count Mihaly Von Zichy; 51 Elegant Soirée by Albert Chevalier Tayler. Italian Trade Centre: p11. Sopexa: pp 8tl, 24tl, 33tl, 37bl, 40tl, 46tl, 54r, 58tr, 59, 63tr. Visual Arts Library: pp 12 Wine Tasting at the London Docks by Augusterre; 45 The Dessert by A Baugin, Louvre, Paris.

Additional photography supplied by: Steve Baxter with Roisin Neild: pp 1, 3, 19, 24tr, 26, 40br, 48. James Duncan: p 53. Michelle Garrett assisted by Dulce Riberio: pp 2, 5, 25, 42, 43, 54t, 55, 58bl. Nelson Hargreaves: p 30. Amanda Heywood: p 34, 49, 54, 56, 57, 61. Polly Wreford: pp 6-7.

Paintings by Madeleine David: pp 8, 9, 15, 19, 20, 21, 32, 38, 44, 46, 63.

CONTENTS

Introduction 6
Cellar Notes 8
Wines for Aperitifs 24
Wines for Parties 28
Wines for Al Fresco Eating 34
Wines for Light Meals 40
Wines for Dining 46
Wines for Desserts 58
Index 64

Introduction

INTRODUCTION

If you enjoy wine and want to expand your knowledge of it, the best way is to record your own experiences of drinking it. Much can be learned from studying the subject, but the successes and failures of your own experiments are far more valuable. Use this book to record the bottles you buy, when you drink them, what food was eaten with it, and how the wine tasted. You will build up a valuable source of information which will enable you to build on your successes and avoid repeating less enjoyable moments.

ABOVE: *A specialist wine shop will be willing to offer advice and recommendations.*

LEFT: *Well chosen wine is a central part of successful entertaining.*

CELLAR NOTES

There's a thrill to buying that first case of wine – perhaps Vintage port, or claret – and storing it away for a few years before bringing out the first bottle to see if it's ready. Keeping basic records of what you have stored away is a useful aid to enjoyable drinking.

Port and claret are traditional choices to be found in many cellars, along with red Burgundies and vintage Champagne. Aged Rieslings can be wonderful, and the finest German Rieslings have been known to age for up to 30 years! There's California's big Cabernets and Australian Shirazes, and don't forget white Burgundy, and those classy Super Tuscans and Barolos from Italy. Add some dessert wines, such as Sauternes, or Hungarian Tokaji, or the sweet wines of the Loire.

Some styles may only need a couple of years resting quietly before they reach their peak of drinking; others require 10 to 15 years. But don't forget, only the best wines are worth laying down, and even then not every year is a "vintage" year. When in doubt, just ask for some advice from your local wine merchant and do some research of your own in the many reference books that are available. It would be a shame to leave that bottle of Rioja Gran Reserva too long.

RIGHT: *Checking the wine before serving in* The Butler's Glass *by Walter Dendy Sadler, 1854-1923.*

BELOW: *Wooden cases of claret from the Médoc commune of Pauillac.*

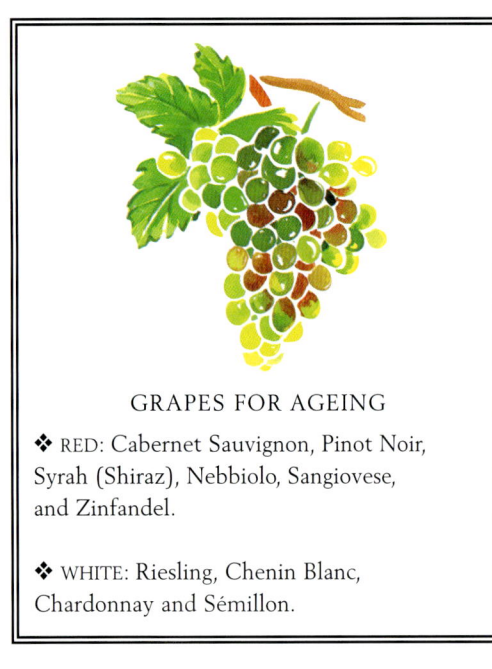

GRAPES FOR AGEING

❖ RED: Cabernet Sauvignon, Pinot Noir, Syrah (Shiraz), Nebbiolo, Sangiovese, and Zinfandel.

❖ WHITE: Riesling, Chenin Blanc, Chardonnay and Sémillon.

CELLAR NOTES

I QUESTION IF KEEPING IT
DOES MUCH GOOD
AFTER TEN YEARS IN
BOTTLE, AND THREE IN
THE WOOD.
RH Barham,
Ingoldsby Legends.

TASTEVIN

These are small, mostly silver, often engraved saucer-shaped bowls. Tastevins were used by the winemaker to check barrel samples in the cellar, or to give buyers a mouthful of wine to taste. Rarely used nowadays, antique tastevins have now become valuable collector's items.

Cellar Notes

Buying wine at auction

The basic rules for buying at a wine auction are pretty much the same as at any kind of auction. Know what you want, set yourself a limit and don't be carried away by the atmosphere! Some auctioneers hold pre-sale tastings, but generally there's the excitement – and an element of gambling – as original, unopened cases and single bottles are sold untouched. Simply poring over the contents of private collections in the catalogues can be a fascinating exercise.

"OFF VINTAGES"

Don't forget that vintage charts can only give a general impression. There are always good producers who can make good wines in lesser vintages; and at more friendly prices too.

For Port ... is incomparable when good ... It has not the almost feminine grace and charm of Claret; the transcendental qualities of Burgundy ... the immediate inspiration of Champagne ... but it strengthens while it gladdens as no other wine can do. George Saintsbury, *Notes on a Cellar-Book*, 1920.

LEFT: *The famous Hospices de Beaune wine auction, held every November in Beaune, Burgundy.*

Vintage charts

A vintage chart such as this one gives a very general guide to how good or bad a year is in any individual region. The quality of a wine from one producer can vary from that of his neighbour regardless of the weather etc. For older wines the quality will vary depending on where it's been kept over the years. The wines here have been marked from 7 to 1, from best to worst.

ABOVE: *Ancient bottles line the wall in a cool underground cellar.*

Cellar Notes

Year	Red Bordeaux	Sauternes	Red Burgundy	White Burgundy	Rhône	Rhine & Alsace (Late Harvest)	Italy (Piedmont)	Italy (Tuscany)	California	Australia (NSW)	Australia (South)
1945	7Δ	7Δ	7Δ	-	-	-	6Δ	7Δ	-	7Δ	-
1947	7Δ	6Δ	5Δ	-	-	6Δ	6Δ	6Δ	7Δ	7Δ	7Δ
1949	6Δ	7Δ	6Δ	-	-	7Δ	4Δ	4Δ	7Δ	7Δ	7Δ
1953	6Δ	6Δ	5Δ	-	-	7Δ	4Δ	4Δ	-	-	7Δ
1959	7Δ	7†	7Δ	-	6Δ	6Δ	5Δ	5Δ	-	7Δ	7Δ
1961	7†	5Δ	5Δ	-	7Δ	-	7Δ	7Δ	-	-	-
1966	6Δ	5Δ	6Δ	-	6Δ	-	5Δ	5Δ	7Δ	7Δ	7Δ
1970	6Δ	5Δ	5Δ	-	6Δ	-	6Δ	7Δ	7Δ	7Δ	5Δ
1971	5Δ	6†	6Δ	6Δ	6Δ	7Δ	7Δ	6Δ	-	2Δ	5Δ
1975	5†	6†	-	-	4Δ	6Δ	3Δ	4Δ	4Δ	6Δ	6Δ
1976	4Δ	6Δ	5Δ	4Δ	5Δ	6Δ	2Δ	1Δ	4Δ	5Δ	5Δ
1978	5†	3Δ	7Δ	6Δ	7†	-	6Δ	6†	6Δ	3Δ	6Δ
1979	4†	4Δ	4Δ	6Δ	5Δ	4Δ	5Δ	-	3Δ	6Δ	6Δ
1981	4†	5†	3Δ	4Δ	4Δ	4Δ	5Δ	-	3Δ	6Δ	4Δ
1982	7†	4Δ	4Δ	5Δ	5Δ	4Δ	6†	5†	3Δ	5Δ	7Δ
1983	5†	6†	4Δ	4Δ	7†	6Δ	5Δ	6Δ	3Δ	6†	3†
1985	5†	4†	6†	7†	6†	6†	7*	7Δ	6†	4†	6†
1986	6*	6†	4Δ	5Δ	4†	3Δ	6Δ	5Δ	6†	5†	7†
1987	3Δ	-	4†	3Δ	4†	3†	7†	5†	6*	5*	5†
1988	5*	7*	7*	4†	6†	5†	7†	7†	3Δ	4*	6*
1989	6*	7*	6†	6†	6†	7†	7*	3†	4Δ	6*	4†
1990	6*	7*	7*	6†	7*	7†	7*	7*	7*	3*	7*
1991	3*	-	6*	3Δ	4†	4*	6*	6†	7*	7*	7*
1992	2Δ	-	4†	5†	5*	6*	4Δ	3†	7*	4*	4*
1993	3*	-	6*	5†	3†	5*	6*	6*	6†	6*	5*
1994	4*	4*	4*	3†	5*	6*	6*	5*	6*	6*	4*
1995	5*	5*	6*	6*	6*	6*	5*	5*	5*	5*	3*

Good vintages not shown: Australia (NSW): 54Δ, 57Δ, 58Δ, 65Δ, 84†.
Port: 45Δ, 47Δ, 48Δ, 55Δ, 60Δ, 63†, 66†, 70†, 77*, 80*, 83†, 85*, 91*, 92*, 94*.   Loire: 47Δ, 64Δ, 71Δ, 76Δ, 85†, 89†, 90†, 95*.   Rhône: 72Δ.
California: 51Δ, 54Δ, 58Δ, 68Δ, 74Δ, 84†.   Sauternes: 67Δ.
Australia (South): 63Δ, 80Δ, 84†.

7 = the best, * = not ready yet, † = mature, Δ = drink soon,
- = not readily available.

© The International Wine & Food Society.

OAK BARRELS

Oak for barrel-ageing comes from many countries, including America for its white oak, but French oak – mainly from the Alliers, Vosges or Limousin forests – is most highly regarded. The typical barrel size is 225 litres, known in French as a *barrique*, unless you are in Burgundy, where it's a *pièce*.

RIGHT: *Wine arriving at London's 19th-century docks, tasted from barrel by the merchants.*

NAME OF WINE/VINTAGE

PRODUCER/REGION

DATE LAID DOWN/NO. OF BOTTLES

COMMENTS

TASTING NOTES

NAME OF WINE/VINTAGE

PRODUCER/REGION

DATE LAID DOWN/NO. OF BOTTLES

COMMENTS

TASTING NOTES

THERE IS NO SAYING TRUER THAN THAT WHICH DECLARES THAT THERE IS TRUTH IN WINE.
Anthony Trollope,
He Knew He was Right.

LET US HAVE WINE AND WOMEN, MIRTH AND LAUGHTER, SERMONS AND SODA-WATER THE DAY AFTER.
Lord Byron,
Don Juan.

Cellar Notes

LABEL ARTISTS

Baron Philippe de Rothschild of Bordeaux Château Mouton-Rothschild first commissioned an artist to design a bottle label for his wines in 1926. Since then, famous artists including Picasso, Salvador Dali and Henry Moore have signed their names to label designs.

LEFT: *A label painted by John Huston to celebrate Baron Philippe de Rothschild's 60th harvest at Mouton.*

NEAR LEFT: *Labels on these five-litre bottles were painted by Baselitz (left) and Francis Bacon.*

NAME OF WINE/VINTAGE
....

PRODUCER/REGION
....

DATE LAID DOWN/NO. OF BOTTLES
....

COMMENTS
....

TASTING NOTES
....
....
....

NAME OF WINE/VINTAGE
....

PRODUCER/REGION
....

DATE LAID DOWN/NO. OF BOTTLES
....

COMMENTS
....

TASTING NOTES
....
....
....

THE BEAUJOLAIS CRUS

The top red wines of Beaujolais, made from the Gamay grape, come from ten villages or *crus*: Juliénas, Brouilly, Côtes de Brouilly, Chénas, Morgon, Chiroubles, Fleurie, St-Amour, Moulin-à-Vent and Réginé.

Cellar Notes

NAME OF WINE/VINTAGE
....

PRODUCER/REGION
....

DATE LAID DOWN/NO. OF BOTTLES
....

COMMENTS
....

TASTING NOTES
....
....
....

LAYING DOWN

The term "laying down" refers to lying the bottles on their sides. This ensures that the wine stays in contact with the cork, keeping it moist and expanded, so that the bottle is completely sealed.

LEFT: *Bottles of Chianti maturing in cellar before release.*

NAME OF WINE/VINTAGE
....

PRODUCER/REGION
....

DATE LAID DOWN/NO. OF BOTTLES
....

COMMENTS
....

TASTING NOTES
....
....
....

NAME OF WINE/VINTAGE
....

PRODUCER/REGION
....

DATE LAID DOWN/NO. OF BOTTLES
....

COMMENTS
....

TASTING NOTES
....
....
....

I WAS CONVINCED 40 YEARS AGO – AND THE CONVICTION REMAINS TO THIS DAY – THAT IN WINE TASTING AND WINE-TALK THERE IS AN ENORMOUS AMOUNT OF HUMBUG.
TG Shaw,
Wine, The Vine and the Cellar, 1863.

AND WINE THAT MAKETH GLAD THE HEART OF MAN, AND OIL TO MAKE HIS FACE SHINE.
Proverbs

Cellar Notes

NAME OF WINE/VINTAGE

PRODUCER/REGION

DATE LAID DOWN/NO. OF BOTTLES

COMMENTS

TASTING NOTES

NAME OF WINE/VINTAGE

PRODUCER/REGION

DATE LAID DOWN/NO. OF BOTTLES

COMMENTS

TASTING NOTES

NAME OF WINE/VINTAGE

PRODUCER/REGION

DATE LAID DOWN/NO. OF BOTTLES

COMMENTS

TASTING NOTES

NAME OF WINE/VINTAGE

PRODUCER/REGION

DATE LAID DOWN/NO. OF BOTTLES

COMMENTS

TASTING NOTES

ABOVE: *The striking roof of the Hospice de Beaune.*

THE HOSPICES DE BEAUNE, BURGUNDY

A charitable institution, the Hospices were set up in 1433 to care for the sick and poor in the town of Beaune. Now wine from the Hospices' own vineyards is sold at a special auction each November, attended by buyers from all over the world.

Cellar Notes

NAME OF WINE/VINTAGE	NAME OF WINE/VINTAGE
....	....
PRODUCER/REGION	PRODUCER/REGION
....	....
DATE LAID DOWN/NO. OF BOTTLES	DATE LAID DOWN/NO. OF BOTTLES
....	....
COMMENTS	COMMENTS
....	....
TASTING NOTES	TASTING NOTES
....	....
....	....
....	....
NAME OF WINE/VINTAGE	NAME OF WINE/VINTAGE
....	....
PRODUCER/REGION	PRODUCER/REGION
....	....
DATE LAID DOWN/NO. OF BOTTLES	DATE LAID DOWN/NO. OF BOTTLES
....	....
COMMENTS	COMMENTS
....	....
TASTING NOTES	TASTING NOTES
....	....
....	....
....	....

THE BIBLE TELLS THAT NOAH PLANTED A VINEYARD AND MADE WINE. "AND NOAH HE OFTEN SAID TO HIS WIFE WHEN HE SAT DOWN TO DINE, 'I DON'T CARE WHERE THE WATER GOES IF IT DOESN'T GET INTO THE WINE'."
GK Chesterton, *Wine and Water.*

The largest Champagne bottle of all is the Nebuchadnezzar, which contains 15 litres of fizz. It is the equivalent of 20 normal-sized bottles.

RIGHT: His Favourite Bin *by Walter Dendy Sadler, 1854-1923.*

Cellar Notes

> WINE SUFFERS A HEAVING BIRTH. IT HAS A ROUGH, GROPING CHILDHOOD. IT DEVELOPS INTO ADOLESCENCE. THEN, IF IT DOES NOT SICKEN, IT MATURES; AND IN THIS IT IS ALMOST HUMAN.
> William Younger, *Gods, Men and Wine*.

> The potency of alcohol as a spirit was discovered by medieval alchemists in their doomed efforts to transform base metal into gold. Believing that they had at last found a vital clue to help their travail, they called the spirit "the elixir".

─❦ CELLAR NOTES ❦─

NAME OF WINE/VINTAGE
....

PRODUCER/REGION
....

DATE LAID DOWN/NO. OF BOTTLES
....

COMMENTS
....

TASTING NOTES
....
....
....

THE CELLAR DILEMMA

No cold, dampish cellar under your house? Do not despair. Keep your wine in a dark, well-ventilated cupboard at a constant temperature – ideally around 55°F/12.5°C. A bowl of water will help to maintain a level of humidity.

LEFT: *A dream cellar, including Imperials and Double Magnums.*

NAME OF WINE/VINTAGE
....

PRODUCER/REGION
....

DATE LAID DOWN/NO. OF BOTTLES
....

COMMENTS
....

TASTING NOTES
....
....
....

NAME OF WINE/VINTAGE
....

PRODUCER/REGION
....

DATE LAID DOWN/NO. OF BOTTLES
....

COMMENTS
....

TASTING NOTES
....
....
....

YOUR STOMACH IS YOUR WINE CELLAR; KEEP THE STOCK SMALL AND COOL.
Charles Tovey,
Wit, Wisdom and Morals, Distilled from Bacchus,
1878.

ONE GLASS WON'T GET SOMEONE DRUNK WHEN HE'S ALREADY HAD A WHOLE BARREL.
Anton Chekhov,
Letters, 1887.

── CELLAR NOTES ──

NAME OF WINE/VINTAGE

PRODUCER/REGION

DATE LAID DOWN/NO. OF BOTTLES

COMMENTS

TASTING NOTES

NAME OF WINE/VINTAGE

PRODUCER/REGION

DATE LAID DOWN/NO. OF BOTTLES

COMMENTS

TASTING NOTES

NAME OF WINE/VINTAGE

PRODUCER/REGION

DATE LAID DOWN/NO. OF BOTTLES

COMMENTS

TASTING NOTES

PRETENDERS TO THE THRONE

Paris, 1976. At a blind tasting competition between California Cabernets and top French reds, the top wine was a 1973 Cabernet Sauvignon from Stags Leap Wine Cellars, California – much to the consternation of the French judges. Three years later at a similar event, a Pinot Noir from Eyrie Vineyards, Oregon, outshone top red Burgundies.

LEFT: *West Coast rivals Old World.*

Cellar Notes

NAME OF WINE/VINTAGE

PRODUCER/REGION

DATE LAID DOWN/NO. OF BOTTLES

COMMENTS

TASTING NOTES

NAME OF WINE/VINTAGE

PRODUCER/REGION

DATE LAID DOWN/NO. OF BOTTLES

COMMENTS

TASTING NOTES

NAME OF WINE/VINTAGE

PRODUCER/REGION

DATE LAID DOWN/NO. OF BOTTLES

COMMENTS

TASTING NOTES

NAME OF WINE/VINTAGE

PRODUCER/REGION

DATE LAID DOWN/NO. OF BOTTLES

COMMENTS

TASTING NOTES

> The Chardonnay and Cabernet Sauvignon grape varieties were first planted in California in 1833, imported along with nearly 100 other French vines by a native of the Bordelais region – Jean-Louis Vignes.

RIPE, GOOD OLD WINE IMPARTS A RICHER BLOOD TO HIM WHO DAILY TASTES ITS TONIC FLOOD.
School of Salerno, *Code of Health*, 11th century.

— CELLAR NOTES —

NAME OF WINE/VINTAGE

PRODUCER/REGION

DATE LAID DOWN/NO. OF BOTTLES

COMMENTS

TASTING NOTES

NAME OF WINE/VINTAGE

PRODUCER/REGION

DATE LAID DOWN/NO. OF BOTTLES

COMMENTS

TASTING NOTES

ABOVE: *"Tasting Notes" for the Cabernet Sauvignon grape: mint, blackcurrant and chocolate.*

FAR LEFT: *Mixed older vintages from an estate in Chianti Rufina, Italy.*

LEFT: *One of the many types of corkscrew which are now available.*

Cellar Notes

NAME OF WINE/VINTAGE

PRODUCER/REGION

DATE LAID DOWN/NO. OF BOTTLES

COMMENTS

TASTING NOTES

NAME OF WINE/VINTAGE

PRODUCER/REGION

DATE LAID DOWN/NO. OF BOTTLES

COMMENTS

TASTING NOTES

NAME OF WINE/VINTAGE

PRODUCER/REGION

DATE LAID DOWN/NO. OF BOTTLES

COMMENTS

TASTING NOTES

ABOVE: *A group of merry cardinals enjoys a lavish meal with abundant bottles of wine.*

IF GOD FORBADE DRINKING, WOULD HE HAVE MADE WINE SO GOOD? Cardinal Richelieu, 1585–1642.

RIGHT: *Cheese, nuts and a glass of port make a perfect combination and are an excellent end to a meal.*

IMPERIAL
20
TAWNY PORT
SANDEMAN
FONSECA
GUIMARAENS
1976
VINTAGE PORT

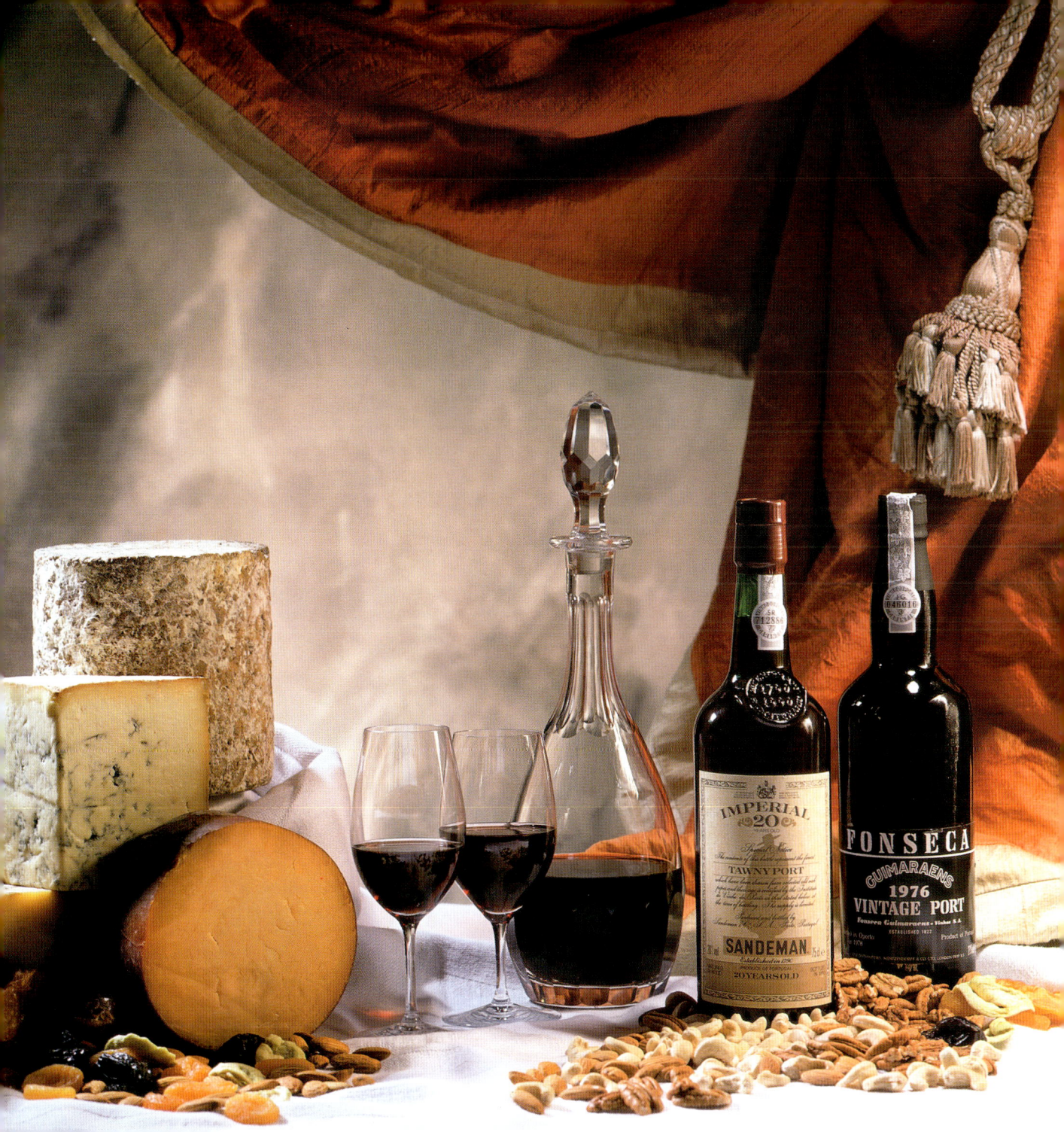

WINES FOR APÉRITIFS

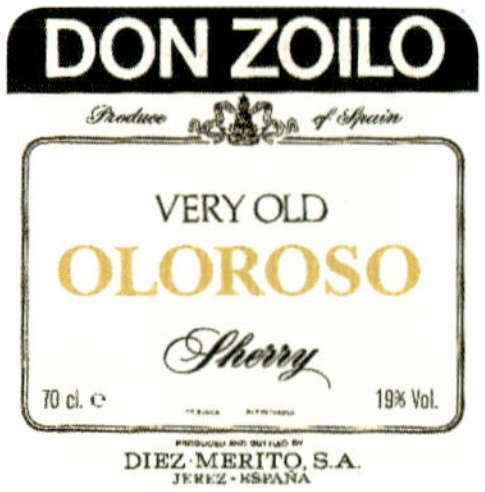

The term "apéritif" is taken from the Latin *aperitivus*, which describes exactly what apéritifs are intended to do – to "open out" or get those gastric juices flowing in readiness for the food to come.

Dry or sweet, still or sparkling, there is a vast range of styles and flavours of wine to offer as an apéritif, all guaranteed to lift the spirits and refresh the palate.

Light, fruity, fresh styles of wine make particularly delicious apéritifs. It's better to avoid heavily oaked wines or "upfront" massively fruity wines – they can be very rich and overpowering and aren't appropriate for an apéritif.

Ring the changes and serve a good, fruity rosé. Cast off those prejudices about sherry being dull and sweet, and savour a chilled fino or, for a richer mouthful, an old oloroso. These dry sherries are especially good with nuts and olives.

There is something celebratory about a tall flute of fizz. There is a wealth of sparkling wines from around the world to choose from, and it doesn't have to be expensive.

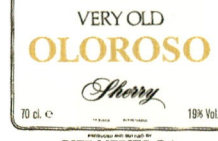

RIGHT: *A classic combination – sherry with olives, cheese and roasted, salted nuts.*

LEFT: *A celebratory glass of sparkling wine.*

KIR ROYALE

Kir is a refreshing, summery drink and eye-catching with its delicate pink hue. The traditional recipe is Bourgogne Aligoté – a dry, crisp white wine from Burgundy – with a splash of the blackcurrant liqueur crème de cassis. It becomes a Kir Royale when made with sparkling wine.

The varying hues of a Kir.

It is said the bowl-shaped Champagne glass was originally designed in honour of France's Marie Antoinette's breasts.

Wines for Apéritifs

Wines for Apéritifs

NAME OF WINE/VINTAGE
....

PRODUCER/REGION
....

COMMENTS
....

TASTING NOTE
....
....
....
....
....
....

LEFT: *Serve a chilled fino or manzanilla sherry with strong-flavoured nibbles such as Parma ham and olives.*

NAME OF WINE/VINTAGE
....

PRODUCER/REGION
....

COMMENTS
....

TASTING NOTE
....
....
....
....

NAME OF WINE/VINTAGE
....

PRODUCER/REGION
....

COMMENTS
....

TASTING NOTE
....
....
....
....

I'VE HEARD HIM RENOUNCE WINE A HUNDRED TIMES A DAY, BUT THEN IT HAS BEEN BETWEEN AS MANY GLASSES.
Douglas Jerrold, 19th century.

— Wines for Apéritifs —

NAME OF WINE/VINTAGE
....

PRODUCER/REGION
....

COMMENTS
....

TASTING NOTE
....
....
....
....
....
....

NAME OF WINE/VINTAGE
....

PRODUCER/REGION
....

COMMENTS
....

TASTING NOTE
....
....
....
....
....
....

NAME OF WINE/VINTAGE
....

PRODUCER/REGION
....

COMMENTS
....

TASTING NOTE
....
....
....
....
....
....

ABOVE: *A bottle of Champagne on ice.*

AFTER TASTING HIS WINE THACKERAY SAID, LOOKING AT ME SOLEMNLY THROUGH HIS LARGE SPECTACLES, "ONE'S FIRST GLASS OF WINE IN THE DAY IS A GREAT EVENT."
William Allingham,
The Diaries,
1862.

WINES FOR PARTIES

Whether you are splashing out for a select event, or stocking up on volume for a big bash, wines that make good party drinks are always worth remembering. But what will please everyone?

Fresh, easy-drinking wines are the answer. Choose wines that are made to be drunk young, that have good fruit. But they should not be too dry nor too acidic. Acid wines won't please anyone's stomach after a couple of glasses, especially if it's a food-free zone.

New World sparkling wines are great party-makers: not too expensive, fruity and fun. Or intrigue your guests with slightly aromatic whites – Pinot Gris, Pinot Blanc – and gently spicy reds – light Zinfandel or Syrah – that get the taste-buds working without sending them into overdrive.

The party officially stopped in America when Prohibition was declared in 1920. Commercial production of alcoholic drinks was outlawed and many wineries went out of business. For some, moonshine and home-made wines kept the party going until the law was repealed in 1933.

LEFT: *Canapés served with chilled wine at a drinks party.*

RIGHT: *A feast for the eyes at* The Tasting: Servers Bringing Wine, *Jan Brueghel. 1568-1625.*

It makes sense to buy by the case for parties: it works out less expensive, as discounts are often offered, *and* a number of high-street chains will deliver free and supply glasses!

Wines for Parties

Wines for Parties

NAME OF WINE/VINTAGE
....

PRODUCER/REGION
....

COMMENTS
....

TASTING NOTE
....
....
....
....
....
....

NAME OF WINE/VINTAGE
....

PRODUCER/REGION
....

COMMENTS
....

TASTING NOTE
....
....
....
....
....

ABOVE: *A tempting array of canapés to accompany glasses of golden-coloured wine.*

LET US DRINK AND BE MERRY, DANCE, JOKE, AND REJOICE,
WITH CLARET AND SHERRY, THEORBO AND VOICE!
Thomas Jordan,
17th century.

BUCK'S FIZZ

That classic brunch-time drink, orange juice and sparkling wine. For an uplifting, tasty Buck's Fizz, spend the money on good fresh orange juice and use a less expensive bubbly.

Wines for Parties

NAME OF WINE/VINTAGE
....

PRODUCER/REGION
....

COMMENTS
....

TASTING NOTE
....
....
....
....
....

Shakespeare's Falstaff suffered for his addiction to "Sack" – sweet wines that were shipped over to England from Spain in the 16th century.

LEFT: Before the Orgy *by Count Mihaly von Zichy, 1827-1906.*

NAME OF WINE/VINTAGE
....

PRODUCER/REGION
....

COMMENTS
....

TASTING NOTE
....
....
....
....
....

NAME OF WINE/VINTAGE
....

PRODUCER/REGION
....

COMMENTS
....

TASTING NOTE
....
....
....
....
....

IF SACK AND SUGAR BE A FAULT, GOD HELP THE WICKED!
William Shakespeare, *Henry IV, Part 1.*

Wines for Parties

NAME OF WINE/VINTAGE

PRODUCER/REGION

COMMENTS

TASTING NOTE

NAME OF WINE/VINTAGE

PRODUCER/REGION

COMMENTS

TASTING NOTE

NAME OF WINE/VINTAGE

PRODUCER/REGION

COMMENTS

TASTING NOTE

NAME OF WINE/VINTAGE

PRODUCER/REGION

COMMENTS

TASTING NOTE

> Burgundy, Champagne, Bordeaux
> Would in many a goblet flow;
> But the Custom House says, "No,
> You shan't drink light French wine,
> You shan't drink light French wine."
> *Punch*, 1851.

WINES FOR PARTIES

READING WINE LABELS

The wine label was introduced towards the end of the 19th century. Before then, wine bottles were kept in marked-up bins and were generally decanted before serving. Some labels are eye-catching and colourful, others simple and easily recognizable. Some tell you clearly what you need to know – especially those varietally labelled "New World" wines; others – notably German and Burgundian labels – can be almost impossible to interpret.

Essentially, the label is there to help us decide if we want that particular bottle.

RIGHT: *Knowing what to look for on the label when you are buying an unfamiliar bottle of wine will help you make the right choice.*

ABOVE: *This wine comes from Dry Creek Valley (California), and its vintage year is 1992. If the wine is a blend from several years a date will not be included.*

ABOVE: *The label will also name the producer, in this case the Rippon Vineyard.*

ABOVE: *Sometimes the label will show the grape variety or varieties – here it is Sauvignon Blanc.*

ABOVE: *Labels state the alcohol level as a percentage by volume – here 13%, and the amount of wine in the bottle – mostly 75cl.*

WINES FOR AL FRESCO EATING

You may enjoy sipping a glass of wine on its own, or sitting down to a wonderful spread in the fading light of evening. There's always something special about eating and drinking outdoors.

Experiment with the wines you choose for such times. Savour a characterful glass of Australian Semillon or a Pinot Blanc from Oregon. On hot days, quench your thirst with a tangy young Sauvignon or lightly oaked Chardonnay – great with salads and smoked fish. Fruity young reds like Valpolicella or Gamay, chilled in the stream perhaps, work wonders with pies and pastas.

Barbecues are a different challenge, with all those tasty, spicy, hot meats and marinated fish, no doubt with a dash of charcoal. The answer is to serve robust, warm-climate wines. Seek out southern French reds and Portuguese reds, as well as Zinfandels and Shirazes. Aromatic, spicy whites hit it off well with marinades.

RIGHT: *Fish straight from the barbecue, served with a glass of chilled white wine.*

FAR RIGHT: *The perfect combination: food, wine and sunshine.*

The Hochheim Königin Victoria Berg vineyards in Germany's Rheingau are named after Queen Victoria. Her partiality to the Hochheimer wines led to their popularity in the UK, where they became known as "Hock".

Wines for Al Fresco Eating

Wines for Al Fresco Eating

NAME OF WINE/VINTAGE

PRODUCER/REGION

COMMENTS

TASTING NOTE

NAME OF WINE/VINTAGE

PRODUCER/REGION

COMMENTS

TASTING NOTE

NAME OF WINE/VINTAGE

PRODUCER/REGION

COMMENTS

TASTING NOTE

NAME OF WINE/VINTAGE

PRODUCER/REGION

COMMENTS

TASTING NOTE

BRITISH WINE

Never say "British" wine in the presence of an English wine producer – it's heresy. A drink labelled "British" wine is a concoction made from imported concentrated grape juice.

FINDING AT THE FIRST DRAUGHT THAT IT WAS ONLY WATER, HE WOULD SWALLOW NO MORE, AND BEGGED MARITORNES TO BRING HIM WINE.
Cervantes,
Don Quixote, 1605-1615.

Wines for Al Fresco Eating

NAME OF WINE/VINTAGE
....

PRODUCER/REGION
....

COMMENTS
....

TASTING NOTE
....
....
....
....

RIGHT: *An al fresco lunch of chilled wine, cheese, fruit and bread. Simple and delicious.*

IN THE PINK

For good-quality rosé, the winemaker starts the fermentation as if making a red wine, keeping the skins and juice together. When the grape juice is "stained" to the shade of pink desired, the skins are removed. In Europe, the only region allowed to blend red and white wines is Champagne.

RIGHT: *Serve a taste of summer with rosé, as well as white, wines.*

Wines for Al Fresco Eating

NAME OF WINE/VINTAGE

PRODUCER/REGION

COMMENTS

TASTING NOTE

NAME OF WINE/VINTAGE

PRODUCER/REGION

COMMENTS

TASTING NOTE

NAME OF WINE/VINTAGE

PRODUCER/REGION

COMMENTS

TASTING NOTE

NAME OF WINE/VINTAGE

PRODUCER/REGION

COMMENTS

TASTING NOTE

> What wondrous life is this I lead!
> Ripe apples drop about my head:
> The luscious clusters of the vine
> Upon my mouth do crush their wine ...
> Andrew Marvell, 1621–1678.

Britain has a "marginal climate" so far as grape growing is concerned. Yet there are around 400 vineyards, which manage to produce some successful sparkling and white wines in particular.

Wines for Al Fresco Eating

LEFT: *A picnic on a Provençal mountainside of French bread, salad, saucisson and a bottle of white wine.*

ONE GRAPE, SEVERAL NAMES

The grape of red Rioja, Tempranillo, suffers an identity crisis in Spain, appearing as Tinto Fino in Ribero del Duero, Cencibel in Valdepeñas and Ull de Lebre in Penedès, while over the border in Portugal it is called Tinta Roriz.

WINES FOR LIGHT MEALS

Crisply acid, fresh and fragrant, a glass of white wine can turn salads and seafood into a feast. Equally, a simple supper at home can be made that much more special with a carefully chosen glass of wine.

You don't need complicated wines to accompany pâtés, pastas or fresh salads. Loire reds or Spanish whites; Chablis or Chenin Blanc from South Africa; California Sangiovese or Barbera – these are all wines that will please the palate and get the conversation flowing.

And if you are eating out, the number of good quality wines by the glass on restaurant wine lists has been growing fast in the 1990s. Gone are the days when all you could get by the glass was house white or house red, which were best avoided: now there's a range of styles at a range of prices.

RIGHT: *A delicate white fish dish such as paupiettes of sole is best with a lightly oaked dry white wine such as Chardonnay.*

SUR LIE

Sur Lie is a winemaking process used particularly in the Loire's Muscadet region. The wines are left "on their lees" (the dead yeasts left after fermentation) through the winter after the harvest, to gain a slight spritz and delicate bready, yeasty characteristics.

RIGHT: *A light Italian lunch is served with a soft, light-bodied red wine.*

HE THAT DRINKS NOT WINE AFTER SALAD, IS IN DANGER OF BEING SICK.
Cotgrave,
17th century.

Wines for Light Meals

Wines for Light Meals

NAME OF WINE/VINTAGE

PRODUCER/REGION

COMMENTS

TASTING NOTE

NAME OF WINE/VINTAGE

PRODUCER/REGION

COMMENTS

TASTING NOTE

NAME OF WINE/VINTAGE

PRODUCER/REGION

COMMENTS

TASTING NOTE

NAME OF WINE/VINTAGE

PRODUCER/REGION

COMMENTS

TASTING NOTE

WARMING UP

The red wine's too cold! Beaujolais or other low-tannin reds actually benefit from being slightly chilled, but "big" wines such as a Cabernet Sauvignon are definitely better served at room temperature. If you can't spare the time to leave the wine to warm up, pour it into a glass and cup the glass in your hands. The added anticipation is worth the wait, which is really surprisingly short.

∽ɢ Wines for Light Meals ɢ∽

COME, COME, GOOD WINE IS A GOOD FAMILIAR CREATURE IF IT BE WELL US'D; EXCLAIM NO MORE AGAINST IT.
William Shakespeare, *Othello, II.iii.*

LEFT: *Serve a hearty winter soup with a warming glass of red wine and chase away any cold-weather chills.*

NAME OF WINE/VINTAGE

....

PRODUCER/REGION

....

COMMENTS

....

TASTING NOTE

....
....
....
....
....

NAME OF WINE/VINTAGE

....

PRODUCER/REGION

....

COMMENTS

....

TASTING NOTE

....
....
....
....
....

CHILLING OUT

Forgotten to put the white wine in the fridge? Pop it in the freezer for 20 minutes. Aim to serve white wine at around 10°F/-12°C or slightly lower, when the crispness and acidity are at their best, but the wine is not so cold that the aroma and fruit are lost.

WINE FOR LIGHT MEALS

AUSTRALIAN WINE

The "father of Australian wine" was a Scotsman, James Busby, who emigrated to Australia in 1825, at the age of 24. He wrote a book on viticulture on the journey out, planted a vineyard in the Hunter Valley, and in 1833 shipped hundreds of European vine cuttings to Australia.

THE RISE OF CHARDONNAY

Until recently, Chardonnay was a rare vine outside Europe. Only 90 acres had been planted in California, while in Australia, in 1967, one desperate winemaker was apparently creeping into another's vineyards at dead of night to get hold of precious cuttings.

NAME OF WINE/VINTAGE
....

PRODUCER/REGION
....

COMMENTS
....

TASTING NOTE
....
....
....
....
....
....

NAME OF WINE/VINTAGE
....

PRODUCER/REGION
....

COMMENTS
....

TASTING NOTE
....
....
....
....

"My dear . . . I have just recollected that I have some of the finest old Constantia wine in the house that was ever tasted . . . so I have brought a glass of it for your sister. My poor husband! How fond he was of it! Whenever he had a touch of his old cholicky gout, he said it did him more good than anything else in the world."
Jane Austen,
Sense and Sensibility,
1811.

RIGHT: *A glass of sweet wine and fine Italian biscuits painted by A Baugin in 1630.*

Wine for Light Meals

WINES FOR DINING

Carefully selecting wines to partner each course can seem rather pretentious. Yet there are times when everyone around the table falls silent and concentrates in delight over the delicious combination of flavours in the wine and food.

Planning a dinner at home with family or friends is the ideal time to reverse the matching theory. Bring out those bottles that you've been saving for "that special occasion" and plan the dishes around the wines.

It makes sense that regional wines and local foods are "made" for each other. Think how well tapas and sherry combine; or big Italian Barbarescos with rich meat dishes. There are a number of classic French partnerships that are based on the local cuisine, too; think of foie gras and Sauternes, Muscadet and oysters, game and red Burgundy.

DECANTING

❖ Decant young, tannic wines. This will release the aroma and soften the wine.

❖ Ideally, don't decant old wines. Open just before serving straight from the bottle.

❖ Bottles that have been laid down need to stand for a while to allow any sediment to drop to the bottom.

❖ As you decant, hold the bottle neck over a light so you can see when the sediment is about to escape.

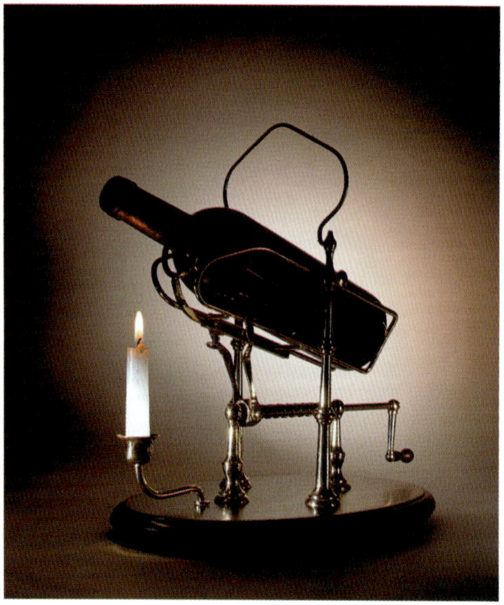

A traditional decanter cradle with a candle in position to check on the sediment.

DO NOT ASK ANY LADY TO TAKE WINE, UNTIL YOU SEE SHE HAS FINISHED HER SOUP OR FISH.
Hints on Etiquette and the Usages of Society, 1834.

RIGHT: *A white wine to complement three different starters is served at this restaurant dining table.*

∽ Wines for Dining ∾

~ Wines for Dining ~

NAME OF WINE/VINTAGE

PRODUCER/REGION

COMMENTS

TASTING NOTE

NAME OF WINE/VINTAGE

PRODUCER/REGION

COMMENTS

TASTING NOTE

NAME OF WINE/VINTAGE

PRODUCER/REGION

COMMENTS

TASTING NOTE

NAME OF WINE/VINTAGE

PRODUCER/REGION

COMMENTS

TASTING NOTE

An urban myth has it that placing a silver teaspoon in the top of an open bottle of sparkling wine keeps the bubble in the wine. Try it . . .

AT DINNER AND SUPPER, I DRANK, I KNOW NOT HOW, OF MY OWNE ACCORD, SO MUCH WINE, THAT I WAS EVEN ALMOST FOXED AND MY HEAD AKED ALL NIGHT.
Samuel Pepys, *Diary*, 29 September 1661.

Wines for Dining

NAME OF WINE/VINTAGE

PRODUCER/REGION

COMMENTS

TASTING NOTE

NAME OF WINE/VINTAGE

PRODUCER/REGION

COMMENTS

TASTING NOTE

NAME OF WINE/VINTAGE

PRODUCER/REGION

COMMENTS

TASTING NOTE

> **SUPER TUSCAN WINES**
>
> A tiny vineyard called Sassicaia turned Italy's wine laws on their head. Planted with Cabernet Sauvignon grapes by Incisa della Rochetta in the 1940s, it marked the advent of the "new-wave" Super Tuscan wines.

LEFT: *With a classic seafood dish, such as this soup, serve a crisp, dry white wine.*

⁓ WINES FOR DINING ⁓

NAME OF WINE/VINTAGE

PRODUCER/REGION

COMMENTS

TASTING NOTE

....
....
....
....

NAME OF WINE/VINTAGE

PRODUCER/REGION

COMMENTS

TASTING NOTE

....
....
....
....

ABOVE: *A perfect finish – dessert and sweet wine.*

RIGHT: *Elegant dining – Edwardian style.*

WINE GLASSES

There is a wide range of wine glasses available – from the traditional cut glass, with matching decanters, to coloured glasses with twisted stems, or simple, light glass. It's not just the look of the glass that counts, however, its design can add to the enjoyment of good wine. Plain, clear, fine glasses, with thin rims, are ideal.

There are specially designed glasses for particular styles of wine, as this picture demonstrates. The obvious one is the Champagne flute, the brandy bowl, or the small sherry copita; there is also the large bowl-shaped Burgundy glass, with lots of room to swirl the wine around to enjoy its aromas to the full.

Wines for Dining

Wines for Dining

NAME OF WINE/VINTAGE

PRODUCER/REGION

COMMENTS

TASTING NOTE

NAME OF WINE/VINTAGE

PRODUCER/REGION

COMMENTS

TASTING NOTE

NAME OF WINE/VINTAGE

PRODUCER/REGION

COMMENTS

TASTING NOTE

TODAY, PRAISE BE TO GOD, WINE WAS PRESSED FOR THE VERY FIRST TIME. Jan van Riebeeck, founder of Cape Town, 1655. Van Riebeeck planted the first vines in South Africa three years earlier.

LEFT: *A rich meat casserole deserves a classic red such as a sturdy Zinfandel or a Shiraz.*

RIGHT: *Serve roast chicken with a soft-edged, quality red such as mature Burgundy, Crianza or Reserva Rioja.*

Wines for Dining

Wines for Dining

NAME OF WINE/VINTAGE

PRODUCER/REGION

COMMENTS

TASTING NOTE

LEFT: *A dish such as squid stuffed with cheese needs a full-bodied white that will hold its own.*

NAME OF WINE/VINTAGE

PRODUCER/REGION

COMMENTS

TASTING NOTE

LEFT: *Lamb is the meat Cabernet Sauvignon might have been made for. Serve the ripest and best wine you can find from Bordeaux or Bulgaria, New Zealand or Napa.*

Wines for Dining

NAME OF WINE/VINTAGE
....

PRODUCER/REGION
....

COMMENTS
....

TASTING NOTE
....
....
....
....
....

NAME OF WINE/VINTAGE
....

PRODUCER/REGION
....

COMMENTS
....

TASTING NOTE
....
....
....
....
....

NAME OF WINE/VINTAGE
....

PRODUCER/REGION
....

COMMENTS
....

TASTING NOTE
....
....
....
....
....

> Dionysus was the Greek god of wine, who wore a crown of vine leaves. In Roman times, known as Bacchus, he began his descent into indulgence and debauchery.

LEFT: *Accompany a rich cheese starter, such as this Italian Fonduta, with a red or a high-acid white.*

IF EITHER A GENTLEMAN OR LADY BE INVITED TO TAKE WINE AT DINNER, THEY MUST NEVER REFUSE; IT IS VERY GAUCHE SO TO DO. THEY NEED NOT DRINK HALF A GLASS WITH EACH PERSON, BUT MERELY TASTE OF IT.
Hints on Etiquette and the Usages of Society, 1834.

Wines for Dining

NAME OF WINE/VINTAGE

PRODUCER/REGION

COMMENTS

TASTING NOTE

NAME OF WINE/VINTAGE

PRODUCER/REGION

COMMENTS

TASTING NOTE

> You find a great number of people in this county who believe, like an article of Christian faith, that an Englishman is not born to drink French wines. Do what you will, they say: argue with him as you will, endeavour even to pour the French wine down his throat, but still, he will reject it.
>
> WE Gladstone, Budget speech, House of Commons, February 1860.

Cloudy Bay put New Zealand on the world wine map in 1986 when it released its first vintage of Marlborough Sauvignon Blanc, a wine that is now sold even before the grapes are picked.

RIGHT: *Combine the salad and cheese course with grilled goat's cheese and mixed leaves, wonderful served with a glass of Sauvignon Blanc.*

Wines for Dining

NAME OF WINE/VINTAGE

PRODUCER/REGION

COMMENTS

TASTING NOTE

NAME OF WINE/VINTAGE

PRODUCER/REGION

COMMENTS

TASTING NOTE

Champagne Pol Roger was the favourite fizz of British Prime Minister, Sir Winston Churchill, who declared: "A single glass of Champagne imparts a feeling of exhilaration . . . A bottle produces the contrary effect."

NAME OF WINE/VINTAGE

PRODUCER/REGION

COMMENTS

TASTING NOTE

LEFT: *Serve a ripe Cabernet Sauvignon with roast stuffed lamb.*

White wine with fish; red wine with meat. Not necessarily! Try Pinot Noir with salmon and Chablis with pork.

WINES FOR DESSERTS

Sweet, or dessert, wines are an often unappreciated delight. Whether rich and high in alcohol, intensely sweet or just touched with sugar, fortified or sparkling, the variety is endless.

Where does that sweetness come from? A number of ways, such as stopping the fermentation before all the sugar has been converted to alcohol, leaving grapes on the vine to "over-ripen" or "fortifying" wines by adding alcohol.

The aristocrats are the *demi-sec* and *doux* Champagnes, the wines of Sauternes and Hungary's Tokaji, the "Nectar of the King". Vin Santo is Tuscany's "holy wine", made from grapes traditionally left to dry under the rafters.

Fine dessert wines are delectable, very lightly chilled and savoured alone. They also make perfect partners for puddings. To finish the meal in style, crack a handful of nuts with the classic digestifs – sweet sherries, fine Madeiras and liqueur Muscats.

NO NOBLE MAN EVER HATED GOOD WINE.
Rabelais, *Gargantua*, 1534.

CROSSING THE EQUATOR

For 150 years until the early 1900s, the fortified Madeira wines were sent on a round trip across the equator in the hulls of ships, during which they were effectively "baked". The heat accelerated the maturation of the wine, to its benefit.

LEFT: *The classic Italian way to end a perfect meal – hard almondy biscotti dipped into a glass of rich Tuscan Vin Santo.*

RIGHT: *A lighter-styled botrytised wine flatters fruit-based desserts such as this crêpe with vanilla-spiced peaches.*

Wines for Desserts

NAME OF WINE/VINTAGE	NAME OF WINE/VINTAGE
PRODUCER/REGION	PRODUCER/REGION
COMMENTS	COMMENTS
TASTING NOTE	TASTING NOTE

NAME OF WINE/VINTAGE	NAME OF WINE/VINTAGE
PRODUCER/REGION	PRODUCER/REGION
COMMENTS	COMMENTS
TASTING NOTE	TASTING NOTE

CIGARS AND SAUCERS

In 1954 the vignerons of Châteauneuf-du-Pape, in the southern Rhône, passed a decree forbidding "flying saucers" or "flying cigars" from "flying over, landing in, or taking off from" their vineyards. This story inspired California producer Randall Graham of Bonny Doon to name a wine made from a blend of "Le Cigare Volant" grapes from the Rhône.

RIGHT: *Sweet wines can even cope with that chilliest of puddings, ice-cream.*

Wines for Desserts

WINES FOR DESSERTS

NAME OF WINE/VINTAGE

....

PRODUCER/REGION

....

COMMENTS

....

TASTING NOTE

....

....

....

....

NAME OF WINE/VINTAGE

....

PRODUCER/REGION

....

COMMENTS

....

TASTING NOTE

....

....

....

....

AND MUCH AS WINE HAS PLAY'D THE INFIDEL AND ROBB'D ME OF MY ROBE OF HONOUR – WELL, I OFTEN WONDER WHAT THE VINTNERS BUY ONE HALF SO PRECIOUS AS THE GOODS THEY SELL.
Edward Fitzgerald, *The Rubáiyát of Omar Khayyám*, 1859.

THE NOBLE ROT

Botrytis, known as "noble rot", is a fungus welcomed by makers of the best sweet wines. It shrivels white grapes on the vine, concentrating the sugar and flavour, and makes unctuous, honeyed sweet wines that are sumptuous with fruit puddings.

RIGHT: *Noble-rotted Chenin Blanc grapes in the Loire Valley's Vouvray region.*

WINES FOR DESSERTS

NAME OF WINE/VINTAGE

....

PRODUCER/REGION

....

COMMENTS

....

TASTING NOTE

....
....
....
....
....

NAME OF WINE/VINTAGE

....

PRODUCER/REGION

....

COMMENTS

....

TASTING NOTE

....
....
....
....
....

ABOVE: *The classic sweet Muscat of southern France, with one of its favourite pudding partners, the traditional Christmas or plum pudding.*

EISWEIN

In December's sub-zero temperatures, often at the dead of night, lights may be seen flickering in some of the vineyards of Germany, Austria and Canada. Pickers are swiftly gathering frozen grapes which will become the intense, sweet Eiswein, or Ice Wine.

LEFT: *Harvesting frozen Riesling grapes in Canada.*

Index

A
Ageing, 8
Alcohol, 17
Apéritifs, 24
Auctions, 10
Australian wines, 44

B
Barbaresco, 46
Barbecues, 34
Barbera, 40
Barolo, 8
Barrels, 12
Beaujolais, 13, 42
Beaune, Hospices de, 15
Botrytis, 62
Bourgogne Aligoté, 24
British wine, 36
Buck's Fizz, 30
Burgundy, 8, 46
Burgundy, white, 8

C
Cabernet Sauvignon, 8, 19, 20, 42, 49
Californian wines, 19, 20
Chablis, 40, 57
Champagne, 8, 16, 37, 57, 58
Chardonnay, 8, 20, 34, 44
Châteauneuf-du-Pape, 60
Chenin Blanc, 8, 40
Churchill, Winston, 57
Claret, 8
Cloudy Bay, 56

D
Decanting, 33, 46
Dessert wines, 8, 58, 62
Dionysus, 55

E
Eiswein, 63

English wine, 36, 38

F
Food, 34, 40, 46, 57

G
Gamay, 34
Glasses, 24, 50

H
Hock, 34
Hunter Valley, 44

K
Kir Royale, 24

L
Laying down, 8, 14
Loire wines, 8, 40

M
Madeira, 58
Mouton-Rothschild, 13
Muscadet, 40, 46
Muscat, 58

N
Nebbiolo, 8
New Zealand, 56
Noble rot, 62

O
Oak barrels, 12

P
Parties, 28
Pinot Blanc, 28, 34
Pinot Gris, 28
Pinot Noir, 8, 19, 57
Port, 8
Prohibition, 28

R
Record keeping, 8
Restaurants, 40
Riesling, 8
Rioja, 8, 39
Rosé wines, 24, 37

S
Sack, 31
Sangiovese, 8, 40
Sauternes, 8, 46, 58
Sauvignon Blanc, 34, 56
Sémillon, 8, 34
Sherry, 24, 46, 58
Shiraz, 8, 34
Sparkling wines, 24, 28
Storing wine, 14, 18
Super Tuscan wines, 8, 49
Sur Lie, 40
Syrah, 8, 28

T
Tastevin, 9
Temperature, 42, 43
Tempranillo, 39
Tokaji, 8, 58

V
Valpolicella, 34
Vin Santo, 58
Vintage charts, 11
Vintages, 10

W
Wine labels, 13, 33
Wine merchants, 8

Z
Zinfandel, 8, 28, 34